Cider with Rosie

THE PLAY OF

Cider with Rosie

BY LAURIE LEE

Adapted by Nick Darke

Notes and questions by Tim Bezant

Heinemann Educational,
a division of Heinemann Publishers (Oxford) Ltd
Halley Court, Jordan Hill, Oxford OX2 8EJ
OXFORD LONDON EDINBURGH
MADRID ATHENS BOLOGNA PARIS
MELBOURNE SYDNEY AUCKLAND SINGAPORE TOKYO
IBADAN NAIROBI HARARE GABORONE PORTSMOUTH NH (USA)

First published in the *Heinemann Plays* series 1993
     95 96 97 10 9 8 7 6 5 4 3 2

A catalogue record for this book is available from the British Library on request.
ISBN 0 435 23295 9

Cover design by Keith Pointing

Original design by Jeffery White Creative Associates

Typeset by Taurus Graphics, Kidlington, Oxon

Printed by Clays Ltd, St Ives plc

CONTENTS

PREFACE

In this edition of *Cider with Rosie*, you will find notes, questions and activities to help in studying the play in class, particularly at GCSE level.

The introduction provides background information on the author, the historical basis to the original novel, the problems encountered in the theatrical adaptation and how these were overcome.

The activities at the end of the book range from straight-forward *Keeping Track* questions which can be tackled at the end of each act to focus close attention on what is happening in the play, through to more detailed work on characters and performance in *Explorations*.

Finally, there are suggestions for further reading of Laurie Lee's books which include his autobiography as well as a volume of essays and articles.

INTRODUCTION

Laurie Lee

Laurie Lee was born on 26 June 1914 in Stroud, Gloucestershire. His father having 'skipped to London', he was brought up with his two brothers and four half-brothers and sisters (from his father's first marriage) by his mother. When he was three, the family moved from Stroud to a new home in the nearby village of Slad. Lee attended Slad village School and then Stroud Central School until 1929 when, aged 15, he left. After working in an office in Stroud he then, at the age of 19, left to walk to London, paying his way by playing his violin in return for small change. On his arrival in London he worked for a year as a builder's labourer in order to earn the price of a one-way boat ticket to Spain. On his arrival there in 1934 he spent a year touring the country on foot, only to be stranded there by the outbreak of the Spanish Civil War.

After being rescued by the British Navy, he returned to England, only to go back to Spain in 1937 to fight in the Civil War. Finding that he had arrived too late, he then travelled around the Mediterranean as an 'odd job tramp', visiting Italy, Greece and Cyprus. With the outbreak of World War II, he returned again to Britain, to work first as a script editor for the Crown Film Unit, then as a Publications Editor for the Ministry of Information, and finally as a Script Editor for the Green Park Film Unit. It was during this time that he published his first volumes of poetry, *The Sun My Monument* (1944) and *The Bloom of Candles* (1947), which consist of lyrical nature poems drawn in part from his experiences in Spain. In 1948, now working as a freelance writer and essayist, he wrote a play in verse for BBC radio, *The Voyage of Magellan*, and he was then employed between 1950 and 1951 to write for the Festival of Britain, for which service he was awarded the MBE.

Lee was by now established in the public eye as a popular writer of poetry and essays. In 1955 he published his third volume of poetry, *My Many-Coated Man*, and *A Rose for Winter*, in which he documented his return to the Andalucia region of Spain in the previous year. His greatest success, however, came in 1959 with the publication of *Cider with Rosie*, an autobiographical memoir of his boyhood and adolescence in Gloucestershire, which immediately became a best-seller.

Following his progress from a three-year-old lost in long grass on the day his family moves to their new home, *Cider with Rosie* records and reflects upon Lee's youth and family, his education both in and out of school, and upon village life, its traditions and the characters who made up the community. In starting to write, Lee was moved to celebrate and 'praise the life I'd had and so preserve it, and to live again both the good and the bad' (*Writing Autobiography* 1975). While the book is broadly autobiographical, it does not follow the line of Lee's life at all strictly: rather, its thirteen chapters rove freely over his chosen content and are organised accordingly to themes – school, village events, vivid and remarkable deaths, his mother, his sexual initiation – in which Lee moves backwards or forwards in time as appropriate.

However, the character of Lee himself, around whom the book is theoretically centred, becomes 'less a character than a presence, a listening shadow ... recording the flavours of the days, the ghosts of neighbours, the bits of winter, gossip, death' (*Writing Autobiography*). This is because *Cider with Rosie* also crucially shows, as Lee noted, 'a world which saw, by chance, the end of a thousand years of life'; that is the way of life in rural, village England. It seemed to Lee that it was more important to tell the story of life in the village in which he grew up, and it is as a social documentary of rural England in the years of 1917–33, as well as an autobiography, that *Cider with Rosie* works most effectively, giving us a window onto a world that is now lost.

Following the success of *Cider with Rosie*, Lee followed it with *As I Walked Out One Midsummer Morning* (1969), in which he describes his travels through England and thence to Spain in the 1930s, and *A Moment of War* (1991) in which he concludes his autobiographical trilogy of that period of his life. Throughout all his work, his independence, both as a person and as an observer of life and people around him, characterises his writing, making it both vivid and accessible to the reader. It is these qualities which account for the success of *Cider with Rosie*.

'Cider with Rosie' – the play

As noted above, *Cider with Rosie* was originally published in 1959 as a prose autobiography. This adaptation by Nick Darke (a writer with the Royal Shakespeare Company, and a former actor) was first performed on stage at the Contact Theatre, Manchester: it has also been presented on radio. The version published here represents the best of both adaptations.

In starting work on the dramatisation, Darke found that the 'main strength of the book lay in the poetry of the prose, but that this in itself was inherently undramatic' and would not work effectively on its own on stage. To solve this problem, he invented the character of Laurie, who acts as the narrator of the action, selected those extracts of the book that are most vivid, and put those words into the mouth of the narrator character he created.

Having made the decision to invent a narrator, Darke

then created the character of Loll, the young Laurie Lee, who plays an active part in the action of the play. He was now free to 'look for dramatic pieces in the book that would work best in the theatre'. The episodic nature of the book meant that Darke was free to pick, choose and in some cases combine episodes on the stage for dramatic effect and, while as a result the nature of the play is necessarily episodic, it is bound together by the character of the narrator as, in effect, he observes his own development in the form of his alter ego Loll from the age of three onwards.

Darke's play is divided into three acts. Act One is set in the new home, starting with the family's arrival there, and shows various incidents leading to Loll's being dressed ready for his first day of school. Act Two is set at the school, for the most part, with flashbacks to Loll's earliest days, and climaxes with the Parochial Church Tea and a notorious local murder. Act Three, finally, is set on a family picnic and shows, in episodes set apart from the picnic, Lee's passage into adulthood at the end of which, as at the end of the book, he is ready to leave the village.

In Performance

In preparing the play, Darke specified that the setting should be 'simple and fluid' and that a 'bare stage and only such furniture and props as are essential' should be used. This is to ease and facilitate the action of the play as it moves, via the narrator's guidance, from episode to episode. Those props and furniture used would, of course, need to be evocative of the period of the play (1917 to 1933/34) and suggestive of the social setting of the play. They would also need to be mobile and flexible, capable of performing several functions in the course of the play. Ultimately, a well-designed production of the play would suggest the nature of the settings through particular, realistic details, and so enable the audience's imagination to create the full picture.

Similarly, Darke notes that while up to thirty-seven actors could perform the play, with an actor to each part, it could be presented with as few as only five actors and four actresses. The implications of this are that Loll would be played by one actor and that the other eight performers, including the actor playing Laurie, would divide the remaining parts systematically between them. Each actor and actress would, therefore, need to present several characters economically, distinctly and effectively to an audience in order to avoid confusion. Costumes used would obviously ease this potential problem, but the performers' use of voice, movement and gesture would need to be both detailed and particular for each individual character played. Again, the audience's imaginative participation is vital in this process.

Of the characters presented, Loll is present virtually throughout the play and grows up from the age of three to the age of nineteen. The story of the play is in effect his story, with the addition of those notorious incidents which he would have known about as he grew up. He is accompanied by the narrator, Laurie, who serves to focus the action of the play and who finally exchanges places with Loll in the final scenes of the play. A successful production of the play would seek to show some similarities through the actors cast in order to heighten the unity and effectiveness of the play. The characters of Loll's brothers and sisters would need to be clearly defined to show both the range of ages and the nature of the character of each. Finally, at the head of the family the mother would, in Act One, need to be shown to be strong and dominating but open-hearted. Her early reminiscences pave the way for her reflections in Act Three as the family starts to disintegrate and she loses hope of real happiness and fulfilment: having been forceful, the character now becomes wistful about her life and resents her daughters' opportunities for happiness. While the character of the mother may not always be likeable, any presentation of the play would need, ultimately, to make her sympathetic to an audience.

The characters of the village that are presented during the course of the play are often met for only one scene. Among the most vivid are the Lees' neighbours, Granny Wallon and Granny Trill, longstanding neighbours who pursue their rivalry to the grave and beyond and who would provide some light relief for the audience; Crabby, Loll's teacher, ineffective and disliked by her class, who is finally put in her place by Spadge Hopkins, one of the older boys at the school; and Rosie Burdock, the Rosie of the title, who provides Loll with his sexual initiation. All would need to be established quickly and economically for the audience.

Finally, the language of the play consists of two easily identifiable types. First, the narration spoken by Laurie is taken from Lee's original book and, consisting of Standard English, would be spoken in an unaccented manner. This would effectively distinguish it from the dialogue of the remainder of the play, which is written in the vernacular dialect particular to the area of Gloucestershire in which Lee grew up. The obvious features of this dialect, which would need to be delivered in the appropriate broadly west-country accent for true effect, are its abbreviations ('Gotta yella roof, Ma!') and its particular, localised vocabulary ('chicken gah').

The content of the play, being autobiographical, naturally demands this realistically appropriate style to the dialogue, which would need to be practised carefully in order for its full effect to be appreciated.

Reading the Play

All plays are written to be performed or, at the very least, read aloud. As noted above, it will only be in a well-rehearsed reading of the play that the nature of its dialogue, heavily accented and colloquial, will be fully appreciated. From this, however, will spring a greater sense and understanding of the nature of the characters as they are heard in action. Arising in turn it will be possible to develop a sense of how the characters might show their feelings and reactions in other, physical ways. It is only through an effective reading of the play that an understanding of the many characters' natures and interactions can be developed.

While the play is divided into three acts, various 'scenes' are easily identifiable within each act; they are usually marked by a change in the tone of the narration. This obviously lends particular scenes or sequences of scenes to detailed study or to reading, rehearsal and presentation in small groups. A useful approach is to read sections aloud first of all to understand the action and relationships; to evaluate and learn from the strengths and weaknesses of the first reading; then to explore and experiment with the text to discover more depth and understanding of the characters.

Following the text you will find two series of questions.

Those entitled *Keeping Track* are intended to help your understanding of the action and characters as the play develops and can be used when reading the play for the first time. *Explorations* are more detailed questions and rely upon a knowledge of the whole play: under the headings of 'Characters', 'In Performance' and 'Extended Writing', the questions in this section may lead to course work assignments (oral or written) or to examination practice. All the questions are designed to stimulate knowledge, understanding and, hopefully, enjoyment of the play.

Tim Bezant

List of Characters

LOLL
(the young Laurie)

LAURIE
(the narrator)

MOTHER

DOTH, MARGE, PHYLLIS
(Loll's older half-sisters)

HAROLD
(Loll's half-brother)

JACK, TONY
(Loll's brothers)

BAKER

GRANNY TRILL,

GRANNY WALLON
(the Lees' neighbours)

FRED BATES
(the milkman)

MISS FLYNN
(a local beauty)

UNCLE RAY

CRABBY
(the schoolteacher)

WALT KERRY,

SPADGE HOPKINS
(Loll's school friends)

MIDWIFE

CURATE

MRS MOORE
(a friend of the family)

ROSIE BURDOCK
(a village girl)

SQUIRE

VICAR

MISS BROWN
(Loll's music teacher)

MAJOR DOVETON

BARONESS VON HODENBURG

BARMAID

VINCENT
(a visitor, formerly from
the village)

YOUTH 1, YOUTH 2,

YOUTH 3
(lads of the village)

HANGMAN

LAD

MAURICE
(Phyllis's boyfriend)

JO, LIZZIE BERKLEY
(girls of the village)

The play can be performed by a minimum of nine (five actors, four actresses) or as many as thirty-seven.

The setting should be simple and fluid, using a bare stage and only such furniture and props as are essential.

THE PLAY OF
Cider with Rosie
BY LAURIE LEE

CIDER WITH ROSIE

ACT ONE

There is a pile of household goods and furniture covered by a tarpaulin. They include a rocking chair, eight assorted dining chairs, a large kitchen table and baskets of crockery, etc.

LOLL sits cross-legged centre stage, LAURIE stands beside him.

LAURIE   I was set down from the carrier's cart at the age of three and there with a sense of bewilderment and terror my life in the village began.

LOLL starts to bawl. Enter FAMILY.

MOTHER   We're here!

DOTH   This it?

MOTHER   Our new home!

MARGE   Looka that roof!

PHYLLIS   Tis yella.

DOTH   Gotta yella roof, Ma!

harry   Thass moss.

MARGE   Made a moss?

JACK   Gotta moss roof!

LOLL screams.

MOTHER   Marge! Doth! Find Loll!

MARGE   What a beautiful garden.

DOTH   Half an acre Mother says.

MARGE   All them berries.

MOTHER   Don't you go eating berries now, Marge, Doth, you'll be sick and there's work to be done. Found Loll? Where's Tony? Jack, Harold, come along. Phyllis, you take the baskets and that. Harold, Jack,

1

hike the table down and run it in boys eh? Chop chop or we'll never get done

LOLL *screams.*

There's Loll again, Marge! Doth!

MARGE *and* DOTH *are in a corner of the garden eating berries.*

MARGE   All right Ma.

MOTHER   Get about it!

HAROLD *and* JACK *contemplate the table at the top of the furniture pile.*

HAROLD   You climb to the top and take it by the top. I'll lift the bottom here by the top and lift. You lift and drop it to the bottom, with me at the bottom. That way 'e'll drop gentle. I'll 'old 'er fast while you take the top by the top and ease 'er to the ground.

JACK *attempts to carry out* HARRY*'s instructions.* MOTHER *returns with a handful of flowers.*

MOTHER   Careful with the legs, boys, they're none of 'em fast.

JACK   Got 'em by the top, Ma.

MOTHER   Keep 'em upright. Isn't it a handsome place, Phyl, we've come to. Pump there look, apple trees, syringa, strawberries over there, see the daisies down the bank?

LOLL *screams.*

Marge! Doth!

MARGE *and* DOTH *are still eating berries.*

DOTH   A'right Ma!

LOLL *screams louder.*

MOTHER   Find that boy!

MARGE   'Ere 'e is!

DOTH   Hiding in the long grass.

MARGE   (*to* LOLL) Come wi' me and we'll stuff 'e fulla berries.

They hitch LOLL *up by the arms.* MOTHER *sees them from a distance.*

MOTHER   Seen Tony?

MARGE   No Ma.

MOTHER   Now he's wandered off. Go down the lake quickly now! Doth!

(MARGE *and* DOTH *drop* LOLL *and run off.* LOLL *screams.*)

Hush Loll! We'll fill the house with flowers Phyl, all the vases and jugs out please, work the pump for water, come along boys.

JACK   Fixed the legs.

MOTHER   Indoors with it now Jack.

MOTHER, DOTH, PHYLLIS, JACK *and* HARRY *carry the furniture, etc, into the house and set up the kitchen.* MOTHER *fills the place with flowers.*

LAURIE   My family was born into a world which saw, by chance, the end of a thousand years of life. A world of hard work and patience, of backs bent to the ground, hands massaging the crops, of waiting on weather and growth. Of villages like ships in empty landscapes and the long walking distances between them. Of white narrow roads rutted by hooves and cartwheels, innocent as yet of the motor car, down which people rarely passed and almost never for pleasure, and the horse was the fastest thing moving.

MOTHER *sits exhausted in the rocker.*

MOTHER   Phew. Now Phyl, glass fishes on the mantlepiece and the framed photograph of your father, where's that?

PHYLLIS   Somewhere –

MOTHER   China dogs? Bronze horses? They'll go in the window, dear, don't you think?

LOLL *crawls around the floor.*

Look at that boy, Phyl. Keep him away from the jugs: there's enough broken crockery as it is on this trip –

Enter MARGE *and* DOTH *carrying* TONY.

MARGE   Found 'im.

MOTHER   (*to* TONY) Where've you been?

TONY   Shootin' crocodiles.

DOTH   'E was down by the lake.

TONY   On the Nile.

MARGE   There's a coot with 'er chicks.

TONY   Big swamps like, and crocodiles.

MARGE   Come on Doth.

DOTH   Where to?

MARGE   Cellar.

MARGE *and* DOTH *exit to cellar.*

MOTHER   (*to* TONY) Now don't you go down the lake again, there's a garden up here fulla lions. Fold the paper, Phyllis, don't crumple it …

(PHYLLIS *is unwrapping crockery and crumpling up the newspaper.*)

… that's to be saved for cuttings.

LAURIE   Suddenly our first day was at an end. The house was furnished. Each stick and cup and picture was nailed immovably in place. The beds were sheeted, the windows curtained, the straw mats laid, and the house was home.

There is a scream from off stage.

MOTHER   Oh damn and cuss, what's up now?

MARGE *runs in with* DOTH *close behind.*

MARGE   The cellar's fulla frogs!

DOTH   There's mushrooms on the ceiling!

MOTHER   And all for three and sixpence a week!

LAURIE   From that day on we grew up. Nothing escaped or changed, and so it remained for twenty years.

Late evening round the kitchen table. MOTHER *is cutting up newspapers.* HAROLD *repairs his bike,* JACK *does his homework,* LOLL *draws,* MARGE *sews,* DOTH *is writing a love letter,* PHYLLIS *is polishing spoons.* TONY *plays with cotton reels. No one listens to what he says.*

TONY   So they come outa this big 'ole, see, and the big chap say 'fie' and said we'll kill 'em, see, and the pirates was waitin' up there and they 'ad this gurt cannon and they went bang fire and the big chap fell down whee, and rolled back in the 'ole and I said we gottem and I run up the 'ill and this boat was comin' and I jumped aboard whoosh crump and I said now I'm cap'n and they all said 'fie' and I took me 'atchet ack ack and they all fell plop in the sea wallop and I sailed the boat round 'ere and round 'ere …

LAURIE   At twenty my father married the daughter of a local merchant, and she bore him eight children of whom four survived, before dying herself still young. Then he married his housekeeper, my mother, who bore him four more, three surviving, of which I was one. He left us when I was three, and apart from rare and fugitive visits, he did not live with us again.

HAROLD   I turned a shaft to a thou today.

JACK   A what?

HAROLD   A thou.

MARGE   Charlie Revell's got a brand new suit. He had it made to fit.

DOTH   He half fancies himself.

MOTHER   (*correcting the pronunciation*) Charlie Rev*elle*.

MARGE   Look Doth, I got these bits for sixpence, I'm going to stitch 'em all round the top here.

DOTH   Hm. Well. Tccchhh tccchhh, s'all right.

PHYLLIS   Dr Green came up to the shop this morning wearing corduroy bloomers.

LOLL   Look Ma, look. I've drawn a church on fire.

JACK   If X equals Y, then Y equals Z …

LOLL   Look …

JACK   Shuddup Loll. If X equals Y …

LOLL   Looka this 'ere church …

JACK   Ma, tell Laurie to shut 'is trap.

MOTHER   Oh I've found a handsome snip for my animal album – an old seal – just look girls, the expression …

TONY   So I went round 'ere and 'e said 'fie' so I went ack ack …

JACK   (*to* TONY) Shuddup.

MARGE   Sshh!

LOLL   What?

DOTH   Hark!

MOTHER   Hush!

They all stop what they're doing and strain their ears.

DOTH   It's him.

MARGE   He's broke out again.

MOTHER   Bolt the door Marjorie. Jack, blow out the candle.

MARGE *bolts the door,* JACK *blows out the candle. The* FAMILY *sits in darkness. The girls giggle.*

MOTHER   Hush! Keep quiet. Don't move.

The sound of chains being dragged up the lane. The girls leap up with curious cries. They stumble their way across the floor and claw back the curtains. They look out of the window as the rattle grows louder, accompanied by the drumming of feet.

DOTH   Jones's goat!

LAURIE   Two words that were almost worship. For this was not a straying animal but a beast of ancient dream, the moonlight-walker of the village roads, half-captive, half-rutting king. He was huge and hairy as a Shetland horse and all the men were afraid of him. Squire Jones kept him chained to a spike driven five foot deep into the ground, yet when nights were bright with moon or summer neither spike nor chains could hold him.

The goat snorts and rages outside the house.

DOTH   Did you ever see a goat so big?

MARGE   I heard he knocked down Miss Chen.

DOTH   Just think of meeting him coming home.

MARGE   Whatever would you do?

DOTH   Have a fit.

MARGE   What would you do, Phyl?

PHYLLIS *is in the pantry having hysterics.*

HAROLD   What about the two-headed sheep?

MOTHER   Talks to itself.

MARGE   It sings in harmony.

HAROLD   They only see it when the lightning flashes.

MOTHER   Lives alone in Catswood Marshes.

JACK   Walt Kerry smells of chicken gah. I 'ad to move me desk.

HAROLD   Hark who's talkin', dainty Dick.

DOTH   Y'know that boy from the dairy, Marge? The one they call Barnacle Boots? 'E asked me to go Spots with 'im. I told 'im to run off 'ome.

MARGE   You never!

DOTH   I said I don't go no pictures with butter-wallopers. Shoulda seen 'is face.

MARGE   Charlie Revell's 'ad 'is ears syringed.

MOTHER	Rev*elle.*
LAURIE	I was not at all surprised when I heard of the end of the world. Everything pointed to it.

Enter PHYLLIS *with a bag of prunes.*

PHYLLIS	The war's over! It's ended!
MARGE	How d'you know?
PHYLLIS	They told me in the stores and they was givin' away prunes!
TONY	Giss one!
LAURIE	(*as the children eat prunes*) I was sure it was the end of the world. All my life was war, and the war was the world. Now the war was over so the end of the world was come. It made no other sense to me.
DOTH	Let's go see!

They all leap and rush out. Loud drunken singing.

LAURIE	We went hand in hand through the rain, up the bank and down the street. Bonfires crackled.

They stop and look over a fence at a bonfire. A WOMAN *jumps up and down in the light of it, with a jug in her hand, releasing primeval utterances of joy. A* MAN *walks up to them, kisses the* GIRLS, *hops, twists on one foot, falls on his back working his legs like a frog and croaks a loud song.*

Then the school chimney caught fire.

The CHILDREN *leap for joy. The revelling dies down and the* FAMILY *returns to the kitchen table.*

LOLL	What's this peace anyhow?
JACK	Food tastes the same.
MARGE	Pump water's just as cold.
HAROLD	House ab'm got no bigger.
PHYLLIS	The village is fulla men standing round in braces and khaki pants smoking short pipes, scratching their arms and staring at the gardens.

The BAKER *knocks at the door. He carries a tray with eight loaves of bread.* MOTHER *lets him in.*

MOTHER   Oh dear.

BAKER   Afraid I need paying today Mrs Lee.

TONY, LOLL *and* JACK *hungrily demolish two of the loaves while* MOTHER *searches in her empty purse for money.*

MOTHER   Jack, run up to Mrs Turk and try to borrow half a crown. I didn't know I'd got so low.

JACK *runs off.* TONY *holds a dead mouse up.*

TONY   Gotta mouse 'ere, look.

MOTHER   Where did you find that?

TONY   In me bread.

MOTHER   Oh my goodness.

BAKER   Still need paying Mrs Lee.

LOLL *takes a nail from his pocket.*

LOLL   'Ere, better 'ave this back.

PHYLLIS   Yes, that came in the last batch.

MOTHER   Will you have some tea? While you wait?

BAKER   Yes. If it's going.

MOTHER   Loll, run and see if Granny Trill's got a screw of tea. And hurry now, the pot'll be boiling soon.

Exit LOLL. MOTHER *puts the kettle on.*

LAURIE   Our house was seventeenth-century Cotswold. It was shaped like a T and we lived in the downstroke. The topstroke, which bore into the bank like a rusty expended shell, was divided separately among two old ladies, one portion lying above the other. Granny Trill and Granny Wallon were two rival ancients, and lived on each others' nerves. They referred to each other as –

GRANNY TRILL *sits in her chair combing her hair,* GRANNY WALLON *bottles wine.*

TRILL   'Er down under.

LAURIE   And –

WALLON   'Er up top.

LAURIE   In all their time as close neighbours they never exchanged a word.

> TRILL *stamps her foot on the floor and* WALLON *takes a broom and thumps the end of it on the ceiling in reply.*

> LOLL *enters* TRILL'S *place.*

LOLL   You at 'ome Granny Trill? Y'in there Gran?

> TONY *joins* LOLL *at the door.*

TRILL   Well I'll be bound. It's you varmints again.

LOLL   Come to visit Gran.

TRILL   You better come in, only mind things or I'll cut you to pieces.

> LOLL *and* TONY *stalk about, poking into this and that.* TONY *puts a cotton reel in her teapot,* LOLL *skims a plate across the floor,* TONY *returns it.*

LOLL   What y'doin' Gran?

TRILL   Bidin' still. Bidin' still and combin' me bits.

LOLL   You goin' bald Gran.

TRILL   Still got me bits.

LOLL   It's comin' out.

TRILL   No it ain't.

LOLL   Look at the dead stuff droppin' outa yer comb.

TRILL   That's healthy. Makes room for more.

TONY   I found a mouse.

LOLL   In 'is bread.

TRILL   Serves 'im right for eating it.

> TONY *takes the mouse from his pocket and drops it in her teapot.*

LOLL   Lotta dead stuff droppin' out yer comb.

TRILL   I got more'n 'er down there! 'Er's bald as a tater root!

(*She stamps her foot on the floor.* WALLON *replies with a knock on the ceiling.*)

Wicked 'ole lump! I'll see 'er gone!

(TONY *is looking in her dresser drawers.*)

Get yer 'ands from me drawers! Them's female things!

LOLL   Come for a twist a tea.

TRILL   Then ask for it.

LOLL   Where's it to? I'll get it.

TRILL   In the back.

LOLL *goes off for the tea.* TONY *stares at* TRILL *as she ties her hair in a bun and puts her glasses on.*

Pass me me almanac off the wall. See what he's got to say.

TONY *passes her the almanac. She opens it and reads in a clear strong voice.*

'A party of scientists will slip down a crevice with certain resultant fatalities.' That's for June. Well if they must poke around them places. 'A murdered cadaver will be shockingly uncovered in a Western industrialised town.' I knew that'd come. 'Crisis in Parliament. House struck by fireball. Riots. Royal surprise. Turkish massacre. Famine. War. The King will suffer a slight infirmity.' He foresees some monstrous doings. Terrible year it looks to be. And he says we'll have hail on Tuesday.

TONY   You a hundred yet, Gran?

TRILL   Nigh on.

TONY   Have you got a Dad?

TRILL   No.

TONY   Me neither. Not 'ere.

TRILL   Mine died. He was killed by a tree over Ashcombe. He was a woodcutter you know. Strong as a giant. He could lift a horse and wagon.

MOTHER   (MOTHER *calls from her kitchen*) Loll! Tony! Where's that tea?

TRILL   We lived in a wigwam made of pine branches. Just me and me dad, deep in a wood. When he was out tree felling I made baskets and sold 'em. We lived there ten years and I grew up into a beautiful girl. Somehow I seemed to send men breathless. But my dad was a careful man and when the timber men came he hid me under sacks so they couldn't see me. One day a tree fell on him. I was fifteen at the time and I heard him shout up in the thicket. I ran up and found him skewered into the ground by a branch. He was lying face down and couldn't see me. 'I'm going, Alice,' he said. So I clawed a hole in the ground and lay down beside him and held him till he died. Took twenty-four hours and he never spoke again.

MOTHER   (MOTHER *calls from her kitchen.*) Damn it and cuss! Loll! Tony!

TONY   (TONY *is entranced. He whispers.*) What happened then?

TRILL   I lay with him long after that. Then some carters came and found us. I stood and watched them roll the tree off him. Straighten his limbs. Then I runned into the scrub and hid, hid for a week near some foxholes up there. Neither ate nor drank.

MOTHER   (MOTHER *calls from her kitchen.*) Loll! Where's that tea?

TONY   Then what?

TRILL   Squire sent some men out to look for me. They found me but I fought like a savage. They carried me down the Manor and gave me a bath, the first I ever 'ad. Took six of 'em to get me soaped. Then they married me to George Trill the gardener. He was a good man, much like my dad but a good bit slower. My dad planted that tree.

(*She rises and walks to the door and points to a tree. She and* TONY *follow the tree up to the sky, craning their necks.*)

Thrust the seed in with his finger.

Back in Laurie's kitchen.

LOLL *comes in with the tea.*

MOTHER My goodness. You've been hours.

GRANNY WALLON *appears with a jug of wine.*

WALLON Hey there Missus.

MOTHER Hullo dear.

WALLON Try this un thun. Tis the first of my last year's parsnip.

MOTHER Oh lovely. Clear as a bell look. (*to* BAKER) Will you have a glass of wine? Save me making tea. Where that boy's to with the money I just can't think. Loll, gather some cups. Will you stay for some, Granny?

WALLON I'll study a cup.

BAKER Where's that mouse to? I'll take that back and try and get a rebate on the loaf.

TONY I gived it to Granny Trill.

MOTHER Good boy.

WALLON Mr Davies is dead.

MOTHER Dead?

WALLON Dead.

MOTHER When?

WALLON This afternoon.

MOTHER That's another one gone.

WALLON I was sitting home last night just countin' all 'as bin took. From Farmer Lusty's up to the Memorial I reckoned twere nigh' on two hundred. There's bin waves of throat cuttin'.

MOTHER   Too much misery in the world.

WALLON   There was Widow Thomas cut in half by a bull.

MOTHER   I heard about that.

WALLON   Two children eaten by a sow. The bacon tasted very sweet so I'm told.

MOTHER   (*as she drinks*) My goodness ... this wine!

WALLON   There's all sorts goes in my wine.

MOTHER   Lord bless you Granny, fancy cowsnips and parsney. You must give me the receipt my dear.

(*Enter* JACK *with the money.*)

At last.

She hands the BAKER *the money. The* BAKER *drains his glass and goes.*

BAKER   See you tomorrow.

WALLON   I'm gone now.

Exit BAKER *and* WALLON.

MOTHER   Now then boys. Clear the table. Loll, time for your violin.

LOLL *plays a funeral march and the* FAMILY *takes up places round a grave.*

LAURIE   Granny Trill was the first to die. They carried her coffin along the edge of the wood and then drew it on a cart through the village. Granny Wallon followed some distance behind. All went well until the lowering of the coffin.

WALLON   It's a lie! That baggage were younger'n me! Ninety-five she says! Ain't more'n ninety! And I gone ninety-two! It's a crime you lettin' 'er go to 'er maker got up in such brazen lies! Dig up the ole devil! Get 'er brass plate off! It's insulting the living church!

Two of the MOURNERS *restrain her.*

LAURIE   Granny Wallon had triumphed. She had buried her rival and now there was no more to do. About two weeks later she gave up in her sleep. She was found on her bed dressed in bonnet and shawl, and her signalling broom in her hand. Her open eyes were fixed on the ceiling in a listening stare of death.

(FRED BATES *the milkman approaches the house. The* FAMILY *sits round the table.*)

A few mornings later we were sitting in the kitchen, waiting for Fred Bates to deliver the milk.

Enter FRED, *with a metal bucket and dispenser.*

PHYLLIS   Where were you, Fred Bates?

MARGE   Never bin this late before.

DOTH   Fine milkman you are.

FRED   God dammit. God dammit.

MOTHER   Whassup Fred?

FRED   Ain't nobody told you?

MARGE   What?

FRED   Who'd a thought it.

DOTH   What?

FRED   I would never a thought it.

DOTH   What!

FRED   I saw it.

PHYLLIS   I smell an occurrence.

DOTH   'E overslept.

FRED   No! I never!

DOTH   What then?

FRED   I was comin' from the milkin'. It was early. First light. And I was passing Jones's pond.

PHYLLIS   Yes?

FRED   Down by the lily weeds I saw something floating.

TONY   Dead rat.

FRED   Well at first I thought it was Jones's goat.

PHYLLIS   No!

FRED   But when I went down closer, I saw staring up at me the white drowned face of Miss Flynn.

LAURIE   Miss Flynn, the Ashcombe suicide, a solitary, off-beat beauty, whose mute, distressed, life-abandoned image remains with me till this day. She was tall, consumptive, and pale as thistledown. A flock-haired Pre-Raphaelite stunner. On walks with our mother we often passed her way, and we always looked out for her.

MOTHER   There are others more wicked, poor soul ... Yoo-hoo, Miss Flynn!

MISS FLYNN *emerges from her house and skips up to* MOTHER, JACK, TONY *and* LOLL. *She strokes their hair and gives them apples. She stares at her hands, then at the boys.*

FLYNN   Such cheeky boys. The image of Morgan they are.

(*She lifts one knee, points her toe, and twists her hair.*)

I've been bad Mrs. Er. For the things I must do. It's my mother again y'know. I can't keep her sick spirit from me. She don't let me alone at nights.

She skips off.

MOTHER   Poor soul. And her half gentry too.

Back in the kitchen, FRED *continues his story.*

FRED   Her long hair was loose. And she wasn't wearing a stitch of clothes. Her eyes were wide open and she was starin' up through the water like someone gazing through a window.

MARGE   Oh, Fred.

FRED   I got such a shock I dropped one of me buckets and the milk runned in the pond. I stood there a bit thinkin' that's Miss Flynn. And there was no one around.

DOTH   What happened?

FRED   I runned back to the farm and told 'em and they come and fetched 'er out with the hayrake. I didn't wait to see no more. I 'ad milk to deliver.

TONY *and* LOLL *leap up and run out. The girls stare at* FRED *sipping tea.*

LAURIE   Fred enjoyed for a day a welcome wherever he went. He repeated his story over and over again and drank cups of tea by the dozen. But his fame turned bad, all of a sudden. For a more sinister sequel followed. The very next day, on a visit to Stroud, he saw a man crushed to death by a wagon.

MOTHER   Twice in two days. He'll see the devil next.

LAURIE   Fred Bates was avoided after that.

LOLL *plays a Russian dance on the violin.* MOTHER *encourages him, the* GIRLS *dance.*

MOTHER   Splendid! Top hole! Clap clap! Now give me another my lad!

LOLL *slashes away at William Tell,* MOTHER *dances round the hearth while the* GIRLS *clap and drum along with the tune.*

LAURIE   When my Mother was seventeen she left home and went into domestic service. As scullery maid, housemaid, nursemaid, parlourmaid, in large manors all over the west. She saw luxuries and refinements she could never forget, and to which she naturally belonged. Sometimes, faced by a scratch meal in the kitchen, Mother would transform it in a trance of memory.

MOTHER*'s dancing stops and she clears and sets the table.*

MOTHER   For dining they would have every place set just so. Personal cruets for every guest, the silver must be arranged in order, a set for each separate dish …

LOLL   No stoppin' 'er now.

MOTHER	First of all the butler would bring in the soup, and begin serving the ladies. There'd be river trout next, or fresh salmon lightly sprinkled with herbs and sauces. Then woodcock perhaps, or a guinea fowl, oh yes, and a joint as well, and a cold ham on the sideboard if you wished. For the gentlemen only, of course, the ladies never did more than pick at their food.
DOTH	Why not?
MOTHER	It wasn't thought proper. Then cook would send in some violet cakes and there'd be walnuts and fruit and brandy. For Miss Emily's betrothal a man came from Paris to do her hair and she had a thousand pearls in her dress.

Each of the children lights a candle, kisses her cheek and says goodnight.

LAURIE	Our mother was a buffoon. Extravagant and romantic, she was never wholly taken seriously. Yet within her she nourished a brightness of spirit, which though continuously bludgeoned by the cruelties of her luck remained uncrushed and unembittered to the end. Wherever she got it from, God knows. But she loved this world and saw it with fresh hopes that never clouded. She was an artist, a life-giver, an original, and she never for a moment knew it.

The CHILDREN *are in bed.*

JACK	Think of a number.
LOLL	(LOLL yawns.) Leb'm 'undred and two.
JACK	Double it.
LOLL	Twenny four 'undred and what.
JACK	Can't do it.
LOLL	I'm gonna count to a million.
JACK	Go on thun.
LOLL	(*He yawns again.*) One … two … three … four … five … six …

The candles are extinguished. The stage is dark.
LAURIE *speaks in a hushed tone.*

LAURIE   My first encounter with Uncle Ray – prospector, dynamiter, buffalo hunter and builder of transcontinental railways was an occasion of memorable suddenness. One moment he was a legend at the other end of the world, the next he was in my bed.

A loud snoring noise emanates from LAURIE *'s bed.* RAY *lies across the bed.* LOLL *wakes and sees him.*

LOLL   Urgh!

MOTHER *appears.*

MOTHER   (MOTHER *whispers to* LOLL.) It's your Uncle Ray come home. Let him sleep.

MOTHER *goes.* LOLL *prods* RAY.

LAURIE   A huge scaly man with thick legs and knotted arms.

JACK *is awake now.* LOLL *turns to him.*

LOLL   'E got barbs on 'is chin.

JACK   Got skin like a crocodile.

LAURIE   He was more full of stories than anyone I'd ever met.

RAY *is awake by now.*

LOLL   You really build them railways, Uncle?

RAY   (RAY *speaks with a Canadian drawl.*) All them and more besides.

JACK   And were there Indians?

RAY   Indians or Eskimos, 'pending on where you was at the time.

LOLL   I never seed an Indian.

RAY   Wildest thing on two legs. They never sleep. Can treck a man for years. Eat once a month.

JACK   What do they eat, Uncle?

RAY   Cactus. And little boys.

LOLL   No!

(LOLL *falls out of bed.*)

RAY   True as I sit here. Boil 'em up with frogs. I had it myself once, found it kinda stringy. Well, gotta be going.

He gets out of bed and starts to dress.

LAURIE   When he got through his money he went back to the railway camps.

LOLL   Where you got to go to?

RAY   See a man about a mule.

LOLL   You ain't. Where y'goin? What for?

RAY   Get me fingers pressed. Tongue starched. Back oiled.

LOLL   Ain't true. You're fibbin'.

RAY   See y'all in the oven. Scrub your elbows and watch out for Indians.

RAY *goes.* LOLL *lies back in bed.*

LAURIE   Soon after, while working in the snow-capped Rockies, he blew himself up with dynamite. He fell ninety feet down the Kicking Horse Pass and into a frozen lake. A Tamworth schoolteacher, now my Aunt Elsie, travelled four thousand miles to repair him. Having plucked him from the ice and snow, she married him and brought him home.

PHYLLIS, DOTH *and* MARGE *enter* LOLL*'s bedroom and turf him out of bed.*

PHYLLIS   Come on. Up y'get.

LOLL   Hoi! Whass goin on?

(*The* GIRLS *dress him and wrap him in scarves.*)

Whass all this! Leave off! Lemme go!

(*They shove a cap on his head. He throws it off.* DOTH *picks it up and rams it down over his skull.* PHYLLIS *puts a hot baked potato in his pocket.*)

Ow!

PHYLLIS Keep it in your pocket till dinner. 'Twill keep ya warm.

LOLL What's goin on? Where am I goin'?

MARGE You're starting school today.

LOLL I ain't. I'm stoppin 'ome.

DOTH Now come on Loll, you're a big boy now.

LOLL I ain't.

MARGE You are.

LOLL Boo-hoo!

CURTAIN

ACT TWO

The schoolchildren sit in rows at their desks. LOLL, *his potato in his pocket, stands near the door. Enter* CRABBY, *the schoolteacher.*

CRABBY Good a-morning, children.

CLASS Good morning, Teacher!

CRABBY (CRABBY *speaks to* LOLL.) You're Laurie Lee, ain't you? Come to join us?

LOLL Yes.

CRABBY Yes, Ma'am.

LOLL Yes.

CRABBY Ma'am.

LOLL What?

CRABBY Never mind. (*She indicates an empty desk.*) Sit there for the present.

(LOLL *runs to the empty desk and sits. He waits, expectant.*)

Ar Father …

The CLASS *repeats the Lord's Prayer under* LAURIE*'s speech.*

LAURIE The village school at that time provided all the instruction we were likely to ask for. Every child in the valley crowded there, remained till he was fourteen years old, then was presented to the working field or factory with nothing in his head more burdensome than a few mnemonics, a jumbled list of wars and a dreamy image of the world's geography.

The Lord's Prayer comes to an end. CRABBY *descends on* WALT KERRY.

CRABBY (CRABBY *hits him on the head.*) Shuffling your feet! Playing with the desk! A-pulling of miserable Rosie's hair! I will not have it! I will not I say! I repeat, I will not have it! Lee!

22

JACK AND LOLL   Yes, Miss?

CRABBY   Jack Lee! The bright one, not you fat-and-lazy, inches in the foot?

JACK   Twelve, Miss.

CRABBY   Everybody!

CLASS   Twelve inches one foot, three feet make a yard, fourteen pounds make a stone, eight stone one hundredweight, twice two are four, one god is love, one Lord is King, one King is George, one George is fifth.

CRABBY   Write a poem, which must scan, on one or more of the following. A kitten, fairies, my holidays, an old tinker, charity, sea-wrack.

SPADGE   What's that, Miss?

CRABBY   Don't interrupt! A sea-wrack is when a ship sinks and people drown.

WALT   Please, Miss …

CRABBY   What is it?

WALT   I gotta stay 'ome tomorrer, Miss. 'Elp with the 'ens.

CRABBY   You may stay at home tomorrow Walt Kerry with my blessing. It is fitting that an individual with the wit of a hen should be tending them. (*to* LOLL) What are you staring at?

LOLL   You're wearing a wig.

CRABBY   I can assure you I'm not.

LOLL   You are. I see it. Tis too square to be hair.

CRABBY *approaches* LOLL.

CRABBY   Look very closely. Is that really a wig?

LOLL *inspects her hair.*

LOLL   Yes.

CRABBY   Well I can assure you it is not a wig, and if you could only watch me getting dressed in the morning you'd know it wasn't one either.

(*The* CLASS *giggles.* LOLL *sniffs.*)

Are you sniffing, boy?

LOLL   Yes, Ma'am.

CRABBY Get out into the playground, have a good blow, and don't come back till you're clear.

LOLL *exits.* CRABBY *stares reprovingly at the class.* LOLL *stands in the playground blowing his nose.* LAURIE *approaches and watches* LOLL *remove his coat and lie on the bench.*

LAURIE As a child I used to boast the rare distinction of having been christened twice. My first anointing was solemn and occurred immediately after my birth.

(LAURIE *looks down on* LOLL, *lying on the bench.*)

I had entered the world in doubt and silence, a frail lifeless lump. The midwife took one look at my worn out face and said I wouldn't las' the day.

MOTHER *and the* MIDWIFE *join* LAURIE *and look down on* LOLL, *who has difficulty breathing.*

MIDWIFE The doctor agrees, Mrs Lee. There is nothing to be done. Just wait for him to die.

Exit MOTHER.

LAURIE My Mother was determined that I should enter heaven. She remembered those tiny anonymous graves tucked away under the churchyard laurels where quick-dying infants were stowed secretly among the jam jars behind the vicar's back.

(*Enter* MOTHER *and* CURATE, *bearing a tea cup with water in. He baptises* LOLL *quickly.*)

This hurried christening proved unnecessary. Secretly, silently, aided by unknown forces, I hung on, though it was touch and go. My most perilous moment came when I was eighteen months old, at the hands of Mrs Moore, a neighbour. My Mother had just given birth to my brother Tony.

(MOTHER *holds the baby* TONY *in her arms.*)

We were all born at home those days, and Mrs Moore had been called in to help scrub the children and to cook the soups and it was while in her care that I entered a bout of pneumonia.

Enter DOTH.

DOTH (DOTH *speaks to* MOTHER.) How you feeling, Ma?

MOTHER Bit tired Doth, but all right otherwise. Say hello to your new brother.

DOTH *peers down at the baby.*

MOTHER This is your sister, Tony – Dorothy.

DOTH Beautiful boy … isn't he a picture? Aw …

MOTHER How are you all getting on?

DOTH All right.

MOTHER Behaving yourselves?

DOTH Yes, Ma.

MOTHER What are you all up to down there?

DOTH Nothing much.

MOTHER Where'a Margery then?

DOTH Yard.

MOTHER And Phyllis?

DOTH She's peeling teddies.

MOTHER What about the others?

DOTH Harold's cleaning his bike, and Jack is sitting on the steps.

MOTHER And Laurie? How's Laurie?

DOTH Oh Laurie, he's dead.

MOTHER (*with a shriek*) What!

DOTH He turned yellow. Mrs Moore is laying him out.

MOTHER No one's gonna lay out our Laurie!

(MOTHER *makes her way frantically across to* LOLL*'s bedside. She stares down with horror at his inert,* *naked, yellow body.* MRS MOORE *is sponging him down*

vigorously, humming as she goes. MOTHER *speaks to* MRS MOORE.)

What d'you think you're doing!

MRS MOORE   Poor boy. He's gone. Gone fled to the angels. I though I'd wash 'im for the box. Just didn't want to bother you, Ma'am.

MOTHER   You cruel wicked woman! Laurie ain't dead! Just look at his healthy colour! Wrap him in a blanket and put him in his cot, you ... you bodysnatcher! Poor boy, saints alive, what are you thinking of!

MRS MOORE *swathes* LOLL *in a blanket and carries him to his cot.*

LAURIE   Somehow I lived, though it was a very near thing. So easy to have succumbed to Mrs Moore's cold sponge. Only Dorothy's boredom saved me.

Inside the schoolroom, SPADGE HOPKINS *shoots his hand in the air.*

SPADGE   Ma'am?

CRABBY   What is it, Hopkins?

SPADGE   I dunno how to spell shears, Ma'am. Like what you does to a sheep. Shears.

CRABBY   How do you think you spell it, Hopkins?

SPADGE   Dunno, Ma'am.

CRABBY   How d'you spell ears?

SPADGE   E–E–R–S, Ma'am.

ROSIE BURDOCK *laughs.*

CRABBY   As you find it so amusing Rosie, perhaps you would care to inform the class –

ROSIE   E–A–R–S, Ma'am.

CRABBY   Precisely so. (CRABBY *speaks to* SPADGE.) Well?

SPADGE   Well what, Miss?

CRABBY   How d'you suppose one spells shears, now secure in the knowledge that ears boasts an A.

SPADGE   Er …

CRABBY   Write it fifty times boy! Shears! S–H–E–A–R–S Shears!

Out in the playground, MOTHER *wipes* LOLL*'s brow with a handkerchief.* LOLL *is delirious.*

LAURIE   Pneumonia was the thing for which I was best known and I made a big drama out of it. But it was not by any means my only weapon. I collected minor diseases also, including, in the space of a few short years, bouts of shingles, chicken-pox, mumps, measles, ring-worm, adenoids, nose bleed, scarlet fever, and catarrhal deafness. With the first hint of returning sickness my limbs would splinter like logs, so that I seemed to grow dozens of arms. Then the bed no longer had limits to it and became a desert of hot sand.

(*The* CLASS *begins to mutter, lending a delirious accompaniment to the narration.*)

I began to talk to a second head on the pillow …

(LOLL *talks and mumbles to himself.*)

It never talked back, just lay there grinning very coldly into my eyes. The walls of the bedroom were the next to go, they began to bulge and ripple and roar …

(*The classroom murmurs gain in volume.*)

… to flap like pastry, melt like sugar, and run bleeding with hideous hues. Then out of the walls …

(*The* CLASS *gets to its feet, and smiling, advances on the bed.*)

And down from the ceiling, advanced a row of tangible smiles; easy, relaxed, in no way threatening at first, but going on far too long. Even a maniac's

smile will finally waver, but they just continued in
silence, growing brighter, colder and even more
humourless till the sick blood roared in my veins.

(*The 'smiles' move closer, more manic, murmuring
louder.*)

They were Cheshire cat smiles, with no face
or outlines, and I could see the room clearly
through …

(*The figures surround the bed.* MOTHER *sits on the
end.*)

They hung above me like a stain in the air, a
register of smiles in space, smiles without pity.
Smiles without love, smiling smiles of unsmiling
smiliness, not even smiles of strangers but smiles of
no one, expanding in persistent knowledge, going
on and on … till I was screaming and beating the
bed rails …

LOLL*'s scream reaches a crescendo, then silence.*

MARGE   'E's bin seeing them faces again.

The smiling faces take on a look of concern.

LAURIE   One night while sweating through another attack, I
was given a shock which affected me with almost
voluptuous awe. As usual my fever had flared up
sharply and I was tossing in its accustomed fires
when I woke up, clear-headed, to find the whole
family round my bed.

DOTH   He's never bin like this before.

MARGE   Never 'ad that ghastly colour neither.

MOTHER   It's cruel, poor little mite.

PHYLLIS   Such a happy little chap 'e was.

PHYLLIS *cries.* MOTHER *comforts her.*

HAROLD   D'you think the vicar would come at this hour?

MOTHER   Better run and fetch 'im.

LAURIE   Perfectly conscious, I heard all this, and was tempted to join in myself. But their strangeness of tone compelled my silence. It was then that I knew I was very ill.

(LOLL's *delirium subsides and he sleeps.* MOTHER *kisses his forehead and leaves.*)

I remember no more of that sombre occasion, I think I just fell asleep – my eyelids closing on a shroud of sisters, brothers and Mother, which might well have been my last night on earth.

(LOLL *wakes up, sits up, puts on his jacket and blows his nose.*)

When I woke next morning, to everyone's surprise, the crisis was apparently over. And save for that midnight visitation, and the subsequent behaviour of the village, I would never have known my danger.

CRABBY *walks to the door.*

CRABBY   Lee! D'you mean to stay out there for the rest of the day?

She returns to her desk and LOLL *runs to his.* SPADGE HOPKINS *mutters to himself, writing laboriously.*

SPADGE   S–H–E–A–R ... shear ... she better look out 'er ... S–H–E–A–R ... shear ... that Crabby. She better, thass all ... S–H–E–A–R shear ... how does y'spell ear? Spadge 'opkins ... S–H–E–A–R ... shear ... so how does ya spell? ... ah sod it ...

CRABBY   Did you say something, Hopkins?

SPADGE   No.

CRABBY   Reading over your poem perhaps?

SPADGE   Yeh. That was it.

CRABBY   In that case, perhaps you'd like to share your work with the rest of the class. Stand up Spadge Hopkins.

(SPADGE *gets to his feet.*)

Read out your poem.

SPADGE   The kitten.
          A furry ball is my kitten,
          Curled up by the kitchen
          Fire. Ready to spring
          Or sleep. It like the things
          I like to eat.
          It isn't like a sheep.
          A sheep you *shear*.

          (*He rings the word out aggressively. The other
          children giggle.*)

          Once a year,
          And use the wool for mittens.
          No, not a prowling, hunting cat
          But a bald and seedy rat
          You'd get
          If you tried to *shear* a cat!

          The CLASS *are all talking to one another.*

CRABBY   Silence! Spadge Hopkins. What were you asked to
          write about?

SPADGE   (*aggressively*) Kittens.

CRABBY   What in fact was the subject of your poem?

SPADGE   (SPADGE *mumbles.*) Dunno.

CRABBY   Sheep!

          (*She stands over* SPADGE *and surveys his work.*)

          A sheep you shear ... once a year ... and use the
          wool for mittens. This, Spadge Hopkins, is a poem
          about sheep ... not kittens ... but sheep, you
          understand?

          (SPADGE *marches from the room.*)

          Where d'you think you're going, young man?

          SPADGE *stops and turns by the door.*

SPADGE   Out, if it's any business a yourn.

CRABBY   Sit down this instant! I won't have it!

SPADGE   Ta ta.

CRABBY *flies at him. There is a scuffle.*

CRABBY   Well don't just sit there, help me somebody!

The rest of the class stares. SPADGE *lifts* CRABBY *off her feet and sits her on top of the cupboard.*

SPADGE   Thass the place for you.

Exit SPADGE *as all hell breaks loose. The children ring the bell and throw chalk and yell and sing at each other, while* CRABBY *shouts and kicks her legs.*

Eventually CRABBY *gets down, but the school is deserted, except for* LOLL, *who sits at the desk he first sat at when he joined school. He sits alone, disconsolate.* CRABBY *goes.* LOLL *rises, kicks his chair, and leaves. He walks home, accompanied by the* GIRLS.

MOTHER   Well, Loll? How was your first day then? Like it?

JACK   He didn't like it, Ma. He's in some rage.

MOTHER   What's the matter, dear?

LOLL   They never gave me the present.

MOTHER   Present? What present?

LOLL   She said she a gimme a present.

MOTHER   Well now, I'm sure they didn't.

LOLL   They did! They said, 'You're Laurie Lee ain't ya, you just sit there for the present.' I sat there all day an she never gave me nothin'. I ain't goin' back there again.

JACK *approaches, dressed in coat and scarf.*

JACK   Comin' carol-barkin' then?

WALT *turns up.*

WALT   What, in all this snow?

JACK   'Course in the snow.

WALT   Milkman come in for tea and 'is eyebrows melted.

More CHILDREN *turn up.*

JACK   An't got none.

SPADGE   There's crows worryin' sheep, swans froze on the lake and tits droppin' dead in mid-air.

ROSIE   What you worried about thun, stick-at-'ome?

LOLL   Who'll be leader?

ALL   Me!

JO   Spadge be leader cus 'e eldest.

WALT   'E can't sing!

ROSIE   Thass settled thun. Spadge leader. Loll 'old the cup cus the smallest gets the most when it come to givin'.

JACK   Where'll us go thun, Spadge?

SPADGE   Er …

ROSIE   Big 'ouse. If we catch the Squire before 'is supper, 'e'll pay us to go away.

They sing a carol.

ALL   As Joseph was a-walking
He heard an angel sing,
'this night shall be the birth-time
of Christ the heavenly king.

He neither shall be borned
In housen nor in hall,
Nor in a place of paradise,
But in an ox's stall'.

The CHILDREN *stop singing and wait, expectantly. The* SQUIRE *totters towards them from a great distance, his footsteps echoing across his hall. Finally he reaches them and shakily places two shillings into* LOLL*'s jam jar.*

LOLL   Two shillin!

WALT   Crikey thass a fortune!

SPADGE   Come on, run!

The CHILDREN *run off, leaving the* SQUIRE *alone on stage.*

SQUIRE   The Parochial Church Tea! … is … is with us …

once again … I suggest … and entertainment …
Another year! Another year comes round! When I
see you all gathered together here …

(*The* VILLAGE *gathers and sits in rows before the* SQUIRE
as he speaks.)

…once more … when I see … when I think … and
here you all are! When I see you here … as I'm sure
you all are … once again … it comes to me …
friends! How time … how you …how all of us here
… as it were …

*His moustache quivers and tears run down his face.
The* VICAR *emerges from behind the curtain and takes
over.*

VICAR	What's the smallest room in the world?
VILLAGERS	A mushroom!
VICAR	And the largest, may I ask?
VILLAGERS	Room for improvement!
VICAR	For our first item, Ladies and Gentlemen, we have an instrumental duet by Miss Brown on the piano and – er – young Laurie Lee …

LOLL *and* MISS BROWN *enter, bow, and prepare to play.*
MISS BROWN *at the piano,* LOLL *with his violin. The
music is on the piano,* LOLL *looks over* MISS BROWN*'s
shoulder.*

LOLL	Music's crooked.
MISS BROWN	Then straighten it.

(LOLL *straightens the music and the sheets fall to the
ground.*)

Tch! Pick it up.

(LOLL *picks the music up and replaces it.*)

Hurry up!

The AUDIENCE *starts to fidget.*

LOLL	Gimme an A.

(MISS BROWN *gives him a B.*)

Thass a B.

MISS BROWN   It'll have to do.

LOLL *tunes up like an ape threading needles. When they are ready,* MISS BROWN *plays like a bolting horse,* LOLL *tries to keep up.*

LOLL   It's supposed to be a lullaby!

At the end, when they stop, the AUDIENCE *goes wild with appreciation. Cries of 'Give us another!' and 'Encore!' They play 'Danny Boy' with all their emotion, dawdling dreamily among the fruitier chords and scampering over the high bits.*

VICAR   Thank you Miss Brown and young, er ... Now, Mr ... sorry ... Major Doveton, who has recently returned from the Punjab, will play us a tune on his Indian banjo.

MAJOR DOVETON *tunes his banjo. A string snaps.*

MAJOR   (*under his breath*) Bugger!

(*He tunes some more and another string breaks.*)

Su-warka bacha!

JACK   (*speaking from the* AUDIENCE.) What did 'e say?

DOTH   What 'e said before in Urdu.

Another string breaks.

MAJOR   Jesus Christ!

(*He rises off his chair, throws his banjo on the floor and swears loudly.*)

Benchud!

He exits, kicking his banjo violently before him.

VICAR   Thank you Major ... er. It is now my great pleasure to introduce our guest star, from Sheepscombe. I am most pleased and delighted to welcome, the Baronness von Hodenburg!

Polite applause. The BARONESS *enters and acknowledges her fans.*

BARONESS   I am goink to sink to you a little ditty I convected myself. Bose veords und music. I may say, iss mine – und zey refer to ziss pleasant valleys.

(*The* BARONESS *plays the piano with gusto, ripping off some startling runs and trills. She sings with a ringing laugh.*)

Elfin volk come over the hill!
Come und dance, just vere you vill!
Brink your pipes und brink your flutes,
Brink your sveetly soundink notes!
Come avay – hay! Life is gay – hay!
Life – is – gay!

Wild applause from the AUDIENCE, *the* BARONESS *acknowledges her adulation by curtsying then bowing deeply.*

LAURIE *steps forward, behind him, the bar is set up, the* BARMAID *serves drinks.*

LAURIE   One Christmas, soon after the First World War, a crime occurred on a night of deep snow and homecoming. The night was cold as Cotswold cold can be, with wind coming straight from the Arctic. We children were in bed blowing on our knees, wives toasted their feet by the fires, while the men and youths were along the pub drinking hot pokered cider, cutting cards for crib and watching their boots steam.

VINCENT *the stranger enters the crowded pub and leans on the bar.*

VINCENT   (*with a New Zealand accent*) Drinks for the boys, Miss, and have one yourself. Just take the money from my wallet and don't give me a shout till it's all run out.

The YOUTHS *look up with interest.*

YOUTH 1   That's good of you, master.

The YOUTHS *walk to the bar with empty glasses.*

VINCENT	I'll have none round here call me master. I know the lot of you. Always have done.
	The YOUTHS *peer at him.*
YOUTH 2	Vincent Green ain't it?
VINCENT	That's right.
YOUTH 1	Thought they packed you off to the colonies.
VINCENT	So they did boys, but now I'm back. So fill those glasses and drink my health, I want this to be a night none of us will forget.
	(*The glasses are full, and the cider drunk.*)
	So what are you boys doing with yourselves these days?
YOUTH 3	Farmin'.
VINCENT	Got your own spread?
YOUTH 2	No. Still slinging.
VINCENT	Stuck in a bog. That's what I call that. Stuck in a bog. And what for?
YOUTH 2	Well …
VINCENT	I'll tell you. Damn all. Whose land are you working?
YOUTH 1	Squire.
VINCENT	He still got his goat?
YOUTH 2	Yep. Still got 'is goat.
VINCENT	It's still alive? It was bloody ancient when I left ten years ago, it was terrorising the village then.
YOUTH 3	Still does.
VINCENT	Well damn me. You can travel round the world, cross continents, live through two wars, make a fortune, lose it, make another one, come home for Christmas and Jones's goat is still trailing his lust through the village. How you boys can stand it I don't know.
YOUTH 1	Thass the way it is.
YOUTH 2	Thass the way we like it.

VINCENT Don't kid yourself. You only think you like it cus you don't know any different.

(*He stops talking and squints at the nearest* YOUTH, YOUTH 1.)

Yeah, I remember you mate. We used to play together at Bull's Cross. Remember the Hangman's cottage?

YOUTH 1 Yeah.

VINCENT With the hook behind the door?

YOUTH 2 Still there.

VINCENT Still standing is it? Where he hung himself I mean.

LAURIE Bull's Cross was a ragged wilderness of wind-bent turves, and one through which I would still not care to walk after dark. It was a curious tundra, an island of nothingness set high above the crowded valleys. Yet its hollows and silences, bare of all habitations, seemed stained by the encounters of strangers. At this no-man's crossing, in the days of footpads and horses, travellers would meet in suspicion or lie in wait to do violence on each other, to rob or rape or murder.

(*A* HANGMAN *prepares his noose, waxing it, ready for a hanging.*)

It was just the place for a gibbet. The times were hungry, the hangman's days were busy. He was discreet and skilful. Night after night he strolled up the hill to load the gallows with local felons. After a routine summons one storm black evening ...

(*A young* LAD *is brought across, handcuffed.*)

... he was handed a shivering boy. Used to working in darkness he dispatched the lad quickly.

(*The* LAD *is hanged.*)

... then paused to light his pipe.

(*The* HANGMAN *lights his pipe, the match illuminates the face of the hanged youth.*)

... in the light he saw the gallows clearly, and in the rain-washed face that stared crookedly down at him, the Hangman saw his own son. To the man who stood by him he said nothing at all.

(*The end of the story is resolved in dumbshow.*)

He just walked back to his cottage, drove a hook into the wall, fixed up a noose, and hanged himself.

VINCENT   We used to swing from that hook.

(*He drinks and places his empty glass on the bar.*)

Fill it up. Used to kick the walls down. Remember there was apples growing through the windows? Place reeked of old beds. Yeah, I remember that.

YOUTH 2   When did you get here, Vincent?

VINCENT   We landed at Bristol this morning. Crossed on the Auckland mutton boat. I hired a carriage and it broke down in the snow. I've walked from Painswick. Mark you that's nothing to me. Christ wi' two thousand acres to call your own you get used to a little walking, eh boys?

YOUTH 1   Two thousand acres, and all your own.

VINCENT   I gotta horse, mind.

YOUTH 2   Yeah, well, with two thousand acres you'd need a horse, wouldn't you.

VINCENT   I'm on my way to give my folks a Christmas surprise. Couldn't pass the old pub without looking in.

YOUTH 3   And weren't it just our good fortune to be 'ere to drink your health?

They place their empty glasses on the bar.

VINCENT   Set 'em up again.

(*The glasses are filled.*)

Yeah, I've done well outa New Zealand. Raised cattle and made a heap of money. And I tell you something boys, it's easy enough if you've just got the guts to get out there and do it. Instead a getting stuck in a bog, like some. I mean, look around you. You're just too damn content with what you've got. You slog for the Squire for a miserable ten bob a week, you live on potatoes and by touching your cap, you don't have a sovereign to rub between you and you see nothing save muck and each other. Maybe Stroud on a Saturday night, am I right boys?

ALL Yep.

VINCENT Too right. I know I'm right. I can see it on your faces. Do you know what I've done? D'you know what I've seen? Y'know what I've made?

(He indicates the pile of notes on the bar and fishes a fat wallet from his pocket.)

That's nothing. That represents two thousand acres of prime New Zealand grazing land. Horses, carriages, meat every day, and I never say sir to no one. Now that's something, eh boys?

ALL Yep.

YOUTH 1 Be gettin along now, Vincent.

YOUTH 2 Nice to see you.

YOUTH 3 Thanks.

YOUTH 1 Seegin.

Exit all. The BARMAID *offers* VINCENT *a lamp as he drains his glass.*

BARMAID Better take a lantern with you.'Tis brave'n dark out there.

VINCENT I don't need a lantern. I've crossed the world to get here, Christ I can manage the last mile without a light.

He strides out into the night. A verse of a carol can be heard in the distance. The YOUTHS *are clustered, heads to the wind, at the stone cross.* VINCENT *walks past. A* YOUTH *puts his arm out to* VINCENT *'s chest, stopping him.*

YOUTH   Well, Vincent.

The YOUTHS *each hit* VINCENT *viciously in turn and walk away. They leave him in the snow, having emptied his pockets and taken his wallet and his watch. They amble off into the night.*

LAURIE   The storm blew all night across him. He didn't stir again from the place where he lay. And in the morning he was found frozen to death.

Lights fade to blackout.

CURTAIN

ACT THREE

It is Summer. There is hay on the stage. The FAMILY *enters, led by* MOTHER. *They are burdened with picnic baskets, cloths, etc.*

MOTHER   No come along Maurice, don't fall behind.

MAURICE, PHYLLIS*'s boyfriend, brings up the rear. He carries a jelly.*

PHYLLIS   'E's all right, Ma.

MOTHER   Best foot forward, mind how you go!

MAURICE   I'm all right, Mrs Lee.

LAURIE   I remember one sweltering August Sunday, Mother said it would be nice to go out. We would walk a short mile to find a nice green spot and boil a kettle under the trees. It sounded simple enough, but we knew better, for Mother's picnics were planned on a tribal scale.

MOTHER   Just look at those pretty what-d'you-call-'ems, those whatsits, Maurice, aren't they a picture? I say, Maurice, aren't they pretty my dear?

MAURICE   Yes!

MOTHER   How's that jelly, Maurice?

MAURICE   Melted, Mrs Lee!

MOTHER   Oh yes, dear, that's nice. Mind that bramble, Tony!

PHYLLIS   It's splashing his suit!

MOTHER   What's that, dear?

MAURICE   It's all over me trousers!

MOTHER   Here we are. This'll do. Put the jelly in the shade, Maurice. Marge, lay the cloth there, under the tree. Boys, gather sticks and light a fire for the kettle, quickly now. Maurice. Sit there and relax, you've been working all week.

PHYLLIS   Leave 'im be, Ma.

MOTHER   Unpack the basket Phyllis. There's a good girl.

TONY	There's a wasp in the treacle – tis all gooey – urgh!
LOLL	Milk's turned sour, Ma.
JACK	There's cake crumbs on the cucumber.
MOTHER	That'll make it all the sweeter now, won't it? We'll have to give Maurice some of that cucumber, eh boys? So he can eat it and think of Phyllis while he's chewing.
PHYLLIS	Ma!

MOTHER *and the* BOYS *laugh.*

MOTHER	How's that jelly doing?
MAURICE	Still runny.
MOTHER	Better drink it then. Pass me the bowl.

MAURICE *passes the jelly across to* MOTHER, *who pours it into mugs.*

MAURICE	(*under his breath*) 'Spose we'll 'ave what's set in the sandwiches.
PHYLLIS	Maurice.
MAURICE	Didn't she realise it would melt in this heat?

MOTHER *hands* MAURICE *a mug of jelly.*

MOTHER	There you are Maurice, drink it down.
MAURICE	Thank you Mrs Lee.
MOTHER	Oh what a picture. What a view. Isn't it a scrumptious day? Green as green. Red as red. Y'know it was a day such as this that the Cripstow Blacksmith proposed to the toffee maker – did I ever tell you this story, Maurice?
MAURICE	No, Mrs Lee. I don't believe you did.
MOTHER	Well, there was this lovelorn blacksmith see, in the village of Cripstow. For years he'd loved a local spinster. She was poorer than poor and made her pennies by boiling and selling toffee. She too was lonely and desperate for a husband but too modest and proud to look for one. As the years passed by she grew more desperate, as did the blacksmith …

JO *enters.* LOLL *rises and leaves the picnic to meet her.*

MOTHER Then one day the spinster stole into the church and threw herself down on her knees

LOLL *meets* JO.

LAURIE So quiet was Jo always. So timorous yet eager to please, that she was the one I chose first. There were others of course, louder and more bouncingly helpful, but it was Jo's cool face, tidy brushed-back hair, thin body and speechless grace which provided the secret prettiness I needed.

LOLL Where y'goin thun, Jo?

JO Nowhere special.

LOLL Let's go down the bank then, shall we?

(JO *looks at him, motionless.*)

Down the bank, like before. How about it, Jo?

(*They walk away.*)

What shall we do thun, Jo?

(*no reply*)

What d'say, Jo?

JO I dun't mind.

LOLL Come on, you tell.

JO No. You.

LOLL *stands. He walks away and then walks back, as if making an entrance.*

LOLL Good morning, Mrs Jenkins. What seems to be the trouble?

(JO *lays herself out, gazes up, scratches her calf.* LOLL *inspects her body from head to toe. She doesn't move.*)

Well that'll be all, Mrs Jenkins. I'll be back again tomorrow.

(*He stands and mounts an imaginary horse.*)

Giddy up.

He clip clops off. Exit JO. LOLL *returns to the picnic.*

MOTHER   Oh Loord she prayed, please be mindful of me, and send me a man to marry! Now purely by chance, Maurice, the blacksmith was up in the belfry, every breathless word of the spinster's plea rose clearly to where he was. When he heard her praying, 'please send me a man', he nearly fell off the roof. But he kept his head, tuned his voice to Jehovah's and boomed 'Will a blacksmith do?!' 'Ern's a man's better'n nern, dear Lord', she cried, at which the blacksmith ran home, changed into his best, and caught the spinster on her way from the church. He proposed and they married and lived ever contented and used his forge for boiling her toffee.

(MAURICE *is staring moonily at* PHYLLIS.)

Maurice you're not eating.

MAURICE   No. Gimme some tart thun.

MOTHER   (*slicing a portion*) Give me some tart! Oh give me your heart, give me your heart to keep. I'll guard it well, my pretty Nell, as a shepherd doth his sheep!

(PHYLLIS *squirms with embarrassment.*)

'Course y'know Maurice when I was in service we'd be called upon to prepare a hamper twice, perhaps three times a month in the summer.

MAURICE   Did 'e serve the jelly in a mug?

PHYLLIS *kicks him.* MOTHER *ignores the remark.*

MOTHER   There'd be tongue and cress and salmon in season. Ham so tender it fell right off the bone. Individual sandwiches no bigger than a calling card and that much champagne you'd have sworn it was a summer shower.

Enter SPADGE *and* WALT. *They play cards, apart from the picnic, with* LOLL.

LAURIE   A year or so later, occurred the Brith Wood rape.

WALT   Betty Gleed!

They all react.

SPADGE She stink worse'n you, Walt.

WALT Bloody dun't.

SPADGE Bloody do.

WALT Rosie Burdoch do.

SPADGE Bloody dun't.

WALT Bloody do. (*He points at* LOLL.) 'E tole me.

LOLL Bloody didn't.

LOLL *hits* WALT. *They roll on the floor.* LOLL *pins him down.*

WALT Anyhow, Spadge's bin wi' Lizzie Berkley.

They stop. LOLL *releases him and they both look at* SPADGE.

SPADGE Bloody ab'm!

LOLL Spadge bin wi' Lizzie Berkley?

LOLL *and* WALT *roll about on the floor roaring with laughter.*

SPADGE Never touched 'er!

WALT She's daft in the 'ead.

LOLL Bloody conkers she be.

WALT Yeah. She'd do.

LOLL (*At length, after a pause.*) Yeah.

WALT She a be all right.

LOLL She'd walk in Brith Wood writin' on tree trunks.

SPADGE 'Jesus loves me now'.

WALT I seed 'er Sunday. She was at it then.

LOLL She'm always at it.

SPADGE 'Ow about it?

LOLL Eh?

WALT Tis like this see ... blummin' well simple. After church Sunday mornin', we nips up to the wood. An' when she come back from chapel, we got 'er!

They ruminate on this.

LOLL   She'd 'oller.

WALT   She's too batty.

SPADGE   She'd think I was one of the 'possles!

WALT   Y'all on thun? Whassay? Owaboutit? It'll 'alf be a stunt, you watch.

LOLL   Sunday thun.

They disperse.

LAURIE   For the rest of the week we avoided each other, but we lived with our scruffy plan. We thought of little else but our coming encounter.

(*The* BOYS *congregate.*)

On Sunday morning, we trooped from church and made our separate ways to the wood.

(*The* BOYS *nod, wink and jerk at each other, then head off to lie in wait separately.*)

When we gathered at last at the point of ambush, the bounce had somehow gone out of us.

The BOYS *leopard crawl and lie silent at their ambush point.*

SPADGE   She ain't comin.

WALT   Seed us first.

LOLL   Seen us and gone screamin' 'ome.

SPADGE   'Er's lucky thun. I'd a made 'er 'oller.

WALT   I'd a run 'er up a tree.

They all stand, relieved.

LOLL   Less go thun.

WALT   'Ang on a sec.

LIZZIE *enters. She carries a bag of crayons.* WALT *lopes across and bars her way. She stops. Everyone stares at each other.* LOLL *and* SPADGE *watch* WALT *put his hand on* LIZZIE*'s shoulder. She hits him twice with her crayons, stiffly, with the jerk of a puppet. She turns,* *falls down, gets up, looks round, and trots off. The three boys melt away as* LAURIE *speaks.*

LAURIE Walt was raped himself soon after, and married his attacker, a rich farm widow who worked him to death in her bed and barnyard. Spadge went to sea and won prizes for cooking, then married into the fish-frying business. They all became members of the Parish Church Council.

LOLL *rejoins the picnic.*

MOTHER And on my Sundays off, Maurice, I used to go to Aldershot to visit my friend Amy Frost – Amy Hawkins as was, from Churchtown y'know, before she got married that is. Well this particular Sunday I'd dressed as usual, and I do think I looked a picture.

TONY Ma.

MOTHER I'd my smart lace-up boots –

TONY Ma.

MOTHER What is it, Tony?

TONY Can I go and play?

MOTHER If you must. Not too far now.

(*Exit* TONY.)

Where was I?

PHYLLIS Boots.

MOTHER – striped blouse and choker, a new bonnet, and crochet-work gloves. I got into Aldershot far too early so I just walked about a bit. We'd had rain the night before and the streets were shining, and I was standing quite alone on the pavement, when suddenly, round the corner, without warning, marched a full-dress regiment of soldiers, Maurice. Would you believe it? All those men and just me! I stood bolt still, I didn't know where to look. The officer in front, he had beautiful whiskers, raised his sword and cried out 'Eyes right!' Then would you

believe, the drums started rolling and the bagpipes
played and those wonderful lads, as they went
swinging by, snapped to attention and looked
straight in my eyes. I stood all alone in my Sunday
dress. Quite took my breath away.

LOLL *leaves the picnic and gathers hay with a
pitchfork.*

LAURIE   The day Rosie Burdock decided to take me in hand
was a motionless day of summer, creamy, hazy, and
amber coloured. It was the time of haymaking, so
when we came out of school, Jack and I went to the
farm to help. I stumbled on Rosie behind a haycock
and she grinned up at me with sly, glittering eyes.

LOLL *stumbles on* ROSIE, *lying in the hay. A flagon of
cider is nearby.*

LOLL   Git outa there. Go on.

ROSIE   I got summat to show ya.

LOLL   You push off.

ROSIE   You thirsty?

LOLL   I ain't, so there.

ROSIE   You be. C'mon.

(*She uncovers the cider and shows it to* LOLL.)

It's cider. You ain't to drink it though. Not much of
it anyhow.

LOLL *takes the flagon and unstoppers it. He lifts it to
his lips and drinks.*

LAURIE   Never to be forgotten, that first long secret drink of
golden fire, juice of those valleys and of that time.
Wine of wild orchards, of russet summer, of plump
red apples, and Rosie's burning cheeks. Never to be
forgotten, or ever tasted again.

LOLL *puts the jar on the ground with a gasp. He is on
his knees. He wipes his mouth and looks at* ROSIE.

LOLL   Rosie ...

She crawls along the hay towards him, puts her
hand in his, and pulls him down on top of her.

LAURIE Then I remember little, and that little, vaguely. Skin
drums beat in my head. Rosie was close up, salty,
an invisible touch, too near to be seen or measured.
And it seems the wagon under which we lay went
floating away like a barge, out over the valley
where we rocked unseen, swinging on motionless
tides.

ROSIE *has taken her boots off, and* LOLL*'s, and stuffed*
them with flowers.

ROSIE I like you better than your Jack.

LOLL Do ya?

ROSIE Or Walt.

LOLL Do ya?

ROSIE Or Spadge 'opkins.

LOLL Do ya?

ROSIE Or the Curate.

LOLL Hell fire!

ROSIE Yeah.

LOLL I telle summat else.

ROSIE What?

LOLL Y'know Betty Gleed?

ROSIE What of 'er?

LOLL You'm even prettier'n she.

ROSIE I know!

LOLL 'Tis getting late.

ROSIE Dun't matter.

LOLL I aren't fussed.

ROSIE 's all right.

He drinks another long draught from the flagon. In
the distance, JACK *can be heard calling 'Loll!'.* LOLL

puts the flagon down, wipes his mouth and puts his face close to ROSIE*'s. They stare in each other's eyes.* JACK *calls again. The lights dim. Dusk. The calling stops.*

LAURIE We kissed only once, so dry and shy, it was like two leaves colliding in air.

LOLL *and* ROSIE *kiss.*

LOLL Cuckoo's stopped.

ROSIE So's the mower.

LOLL Gyat. Dun't matter.

They lie back in the hay, holding hands.

LAURIE Still we lay in our wagon of grass tugging at each other's hands while her husky, perilous whisper drugged me and the cider beat gongs in my head.

They get up and stumble towards home.

LOLL See them nettles?

ROSIE Mm.

LOLL *rolls his sleeve up and plunges his bare forearm into a clump of nettles.*

LOLL See?

ROSIE Mmm.

LOLL Gat. Dunnurt.

LAURIE The shifting lane lassoed my feet and tried to trip me up.

LOLL (LOLL *shouts.*) Hyhyhyhyhyiah!

(*He punches the air and trips, falls flat on his face. He gets up.*)

See?

ROSIE Mmm.

LOLL Dunnurt.

They stand on the bank of the lake, staring into the water.

LAURIE	The lake, as we passed it, rose hissing with waves and tried to drown us amongst its cannibal fish.
LOLL	See them otters?
ROSIE	No.
LOLL	I know where the otters are. I dived in and seed a pike.
ROSIE	Mmm.
LOLL	Big pike you. Damn big pike. Big as Jones's goat. I got'n by the tail. Spadge never got the bugger by the tail! Did a! Rosie! Rosie! Where are 'e! Damme the trees is movin now! Ha ha! See the bush there look! See the stars! Rosie!

ROSIE *has vanished.*

JACK	(*from offstage*) Loll!
LOLL	(*sings*) Fierce raged the tempest!

(LOLL *sings the hymn, drunkenly and loud.* HAROLD *and* JACK *approach, stealthily. They grab* LOLL *from behind.*)

Oy!

HAROLD	Come on you.
JACK	Where the hella you bin?
HAROLD	Drinkin'.
JACK	He's soakin wet.
HAROLD	Cider.
JACK	You bin wi' Rosie?
LOLL	Rosie! Rosie!

The picnic resumes. It is late afternoon and the shadows are long. The food eaten.

MOTHER	He was proud of me then, your father. I could make him laugh. 'Nance, you're a killer,' he'd say. He used to sit on the doorstep quite helpless with laughter at the stories I told him. He admired me too. He admired my looks.

She hums to herself. MAURICE *shifts closer to* PHYLLIS.

MAURICE   (*He whispers.*) Come on, Phyl.

PHYLLIS   We can't.

MAURICE   Leave 'er to 'er own thoughts. She's miles away.

MAURICE *and* PHYLLIS *rise and sneak away. The picnic is gathered up and carried home.*

LAURIE   When the girls got engaged, heavy blushes followed as the rings were shown to the family.

PHYLLIS *returns,* MARGE *and* DOTH *gather round.* PHYLLIS *shows them her engagement ring.*

PHYLLIS   It's a cluster of brilliants. Cost more'n two pounds.

MARGE   Aw, it's beautiful.

DOTH   Where did 'e get it?

PHYLLIS   Gloucester market.

As LAURIE *speaks, the house is set up.* LOLL *sits at the table, drawing,* MOTHER *sits in the rocker near the fire, reading the newspaper and cutting out,* MARGE *and* DOTH *sit around sewing and reading.*

LAURIE   Now that things were official, there was more sitting in the dark and a visible increase in tensions. The girls were grown and wished to be gone. They were in love and had found their men. Impatience nagged at them all, until in one case it suddenly exploded.

The back door opens and slams shut.

PHYLLIS   (*from offstage*) 'ome Ma!

LAURIE   She arrived with her boy, which seemed unusual, as it wasn't his calling night.

Enter PHYLLIS *and* MAURICE.

MOTHER   Well take your coat off. Sit down.

MAURICE   (*frozenly*) No, thank you.

MOTHER   Well don't just stand there, stiff as stiff can be.

MAURICE   I'm all right Mrs Lee, I assure you.

PHYLLIS	Ma, we've been thinkin'.

LOLL *stops drawing and looks up.* MARGE *and* DOTH *stop sewing and reading and look up.*

MOTHER	Yes dear?
PHYLLIS	Tis time we got wed. I wanna leave 'ome.
MOTHER	Don't talk so daft.
PHYLLIS	I aren't talkin –
MOTHER	Yes, you are!
PHYLLIS	You're the one oo's daft.
MOTHER	You don't none of you know what I feel.
DOTH	Yes, we do.
MOTHER	It's cruel. Cruel to hear her talk like that.
PHYLLIS	Like what?
MOTHER	I never had a proper chance –
PHYLLIS	It's no good Ma –
MOTHER	Never!
PHYLLIS	We've made up our minds.
MOTHER	Come and sit down and don't act so silly.
MAURICE	She's just about had enough, Mrs Lee.
MOTHER	She doesn't know what she's talking about!
MAURICE	It's time she was out of it all.
MARGE	All what?
PHYLLIS	You stay outa this.
MOTHER	It's a scandal, you coming in like this –
PHYLLIS	Who?
DOTH	Him.
MARGE	What about him?
MOTHER	He just walks in –
PHYLLIS	(*to* DOTH) What about you, come to that!
MARGE	Who does he think he is?
MAURICE	Whose side are you on?

DOTH   (*to* PHYLLIS) You think the whole place is just run for you –

PHYLLIS   Hark who's talkin!

MAURICE   We don't!

MOTHER   Oh yes you do!

PHYLLIS   We never!

MAURICE   Come on girl, I've 'ad enough!

MOTHER   You dare step outside that door!

MAURICE   Come on!

MOTHER   You dare!

> MAURICE *pulls* PHYLLIS *towards the door.* MOTHER *howls.* DOTH *and* MARGE *run at* MAURICE, *furniture falls and a scuffle breaks out.* MOTHER, DOTH *and* MARGE *bounce* MAURICE *against the wall by the throat.* PHYLLIS, *screaming, tries to pull them off.* JACK *and* TONY *appear at the bottom of the stairs.*

PHYLLIS   Let him go!

MAURICE   (*strangled*) Leave go!

PHYLLIS   He can't breathe.

> LOLL, TONY *and* JACK *spring at* MAURICE *and join in the fight. But by the time they get to him the fight is over.* MAURICE *bends over, panting hard and feeling his throat.*

MAURICE   Christ. Jesus Christ.

LAURIE   He had tried to carry off our willing sister and we'd all nearly killed him.

MOTHER   Oh Maurice. Dear boy! Forgive me. Oh forgive me, Maurice!

> (*She flings her arms round his neck and nearly strangles him afresh with affection.*)

         There there.

MAURICE   It's all right.

MOTHER   We're all friends now, aren't we?

PHYLLIS   Oh Mother –

MOTHER   Dear girl. Dear boy.

MARGE   There there.

MARGE *helps* MOTHER *back to the rocker, where she resumes taking cuttings from the paper.* PHYLLIS *and* MAURICE *disappear.* DOTH, TONY, JACK *and* MARGE *melt away into the shadows, leaving* LOLL *alone with* MOTHER.

MOTHER   He really loved me then, y'know? Come on Nance, he'd say, take out your pins …

(*She lets her hair down.*)

… let your hair down, let's see it shine. He loved my hair. It had gold lights in it then and it hung right down my back, so I'd sit in the window and shake it over my shoulders. And he'd twist it and arrange it so that it caught the sun and he'd just sit and gaze and gaze.

LAURIE   The three or four years my mother spent with my father she fed on for the rest of her life.

MOTHER   He'd clear all his books away, 'Come on, Nance', he'd say, 'I've had enough of them. Come and sing us a song.' We'd go to the piano and I'd sit on his lap, and he'd play with his arms around me. And I'd sing Killarney or Only a Rose. They were his favourites then.

LAURIE   She'd smile and look down the weed-choked path as though she saw him coming back. But he was gone for good. The girls were to marry, and one by one they left home. Now she was alone and her idiosyncrasies spread.

LOLL *stands up from the table and walks out, past* MOTHER, *leaving her alone with* LAURIE.)

Her plantpots and newspapers, muddles and scrapbooks extended further throughout the house. She read more now and never went to bed, merely slept upright in her chair. Her days and nights were no longer divided nor harassed by children. She would sleep for an hour, rise, scrub the floor, or go wooding in the middle of the night. Like Granny Trill, she began to ignore all time and do what she would when she wished. I remember coming home in the middle of the war, arriving about two in the morning.

LAURIE *enters the room,* MOTHER *is sitting in the rocker, reading a newspaper.*

MOTHER Ah. Son. Didn't know you were coming. Come and have a look at this.

LAURIE I'm very tired. I must go to bed.

MOTHER You run along. I'll get you some dinner.

LAURIE Wait till morning Mother. It's two o'clock.

(*He kisses her goodnight and walks upstairs.*)

I went to bed and fell into an exhausted sleep.

LAURIE *lies down.* MOTHER *climbs the stairs with a tray.*

MOTHER I got you your supper, son. Wake up.

(LAURIE *wakes and sits up in bed, rubbing his eyes.*)

Veg soup, a big stew, and a pudding, all right?

LAURIE Uh?

MOTHER Eat up, dear. Can't let it go to waste.

LAURIE She'd spent half the night preparing it.

MOTHER Goodnight son.

MOTHER *returns downstairs and sits in the rocker.*

LAURIE Then suddenly our absent father died, cranking his car in a Mordern suburb. And with his death, which was also the death of hope, our mother gave up her life. Their long separation had come to an end, and it was the coldness of that which killed her. She had raised two families, faithfully and alone, had waited thirty-five years for his praise. And through all that time she had clung to one fantasy, that aged and broken, and at last in need, he might one day return to her. His death killed that promise, and also ended her reason. She never mentioned him again, but spoke to shades, saw visions, and then she died.

The FAMILY *enters the room and between them they lift* MOTHER *out of her chair, and lay her out.* LOLL *emerges from the group and stands beside* LAURIE.

LOLL   As for me ... for me, the grass grew longer, and more sorrowful, and the trees were surfaced like flesh, and girls were no longer to be treated lightly but were creatures of commanding sadness, and all journeys through the valley were now made alone, with passion in every bush, and the motions of wind and cloud and stars were suddenly for myself alone, and voices elected me of all men living and called me to deliver the world ...

(*The company starts to sing* 'As I walked out'.)

... and I groaned from solitude and made up poems from intense abstraction, hour after unmarked hour.

LAURIE   And the poems I made, which I never remembered, were the first and last of that time.

The song comes to an end as the lights fade.

THE PLAY ENDS

QUESTIONS AND EXPLORATIONS

1 Keeping Track

The questions in this section are designed to help your reading and understanding of the play in the areas of plot, character, structure and interaction. They may be used as you read the play or afterwards, for discussion or for writing. Some are developed and expanded in the *Explorations* section.

Act One

1 What would the audience see at the beginning of Act One?

2 How would Loll be dressed?

3 What stage directions would you add to the script to describe the activity that takes place as the family move into their new home?

4 How would Jack react to Harold's instructions about the table?

5 What do we learn about the Lees' new home?

6 How would the actor playing Loll show the character to the audience?

7 What would Laurie be doing during this scene?

8 What do we learn about the character of Mother during the moving-in scene?

9 And what do we learn about the rest of the family during the evening scene?

10 How do the members of the family react to Jones's goat?

11 How does the family react to the news that World War I is over? And how does the village celebrate?

12 What does the baker's visit reveal about the Lee family?

13 What do we learn about Granny Trill? How would the character be shown to an audience?

14 What do we learn about Granny Wallon? And how would her character be shown to an audience?

15 What sort of character is Fred Bates the milkman? And how does the family react to his news?

16 What do we learn about Mother's past?

17 How would the bedtime sequence be staged?

18 How would the actor playing Uncle Ray show the character to an audience?

19 How do Jack and Loll react to him?

20 How does Loll react to him?

21 How does Loll react to being dressed for school?

Act Two

1 What would the audience see at the beginning of Act Two?

2 What would be happening in the schoolroom before Crabby's entrance?

3 How would the actress playing Crabby show the character to an audience?

4 What sort of education do the village children receive?

5 How would the flashback in the playground be staged?

6 What do the school children do during Loll's delirious illness?

7 What do we learn about Spadge Hopkins?

8 How does the class react to Spadge's treatment of Crabby?

9 How would an audience react to Loll's return from school?

10 How would the children sing the carol?

11 How would the actor playing the Squire show his character to the audience?

12 How would the relationship between Loll and Miss Brown be shown? How would the villagers react?

13 How would the Baroness von Hodenburg present herself to her audience?

14 How does the tone of the play change after the Parochial Church Tea?

15 What sort of a character is Vincent?

16 And how do the village youths react to him?

17 How would the story of the hangman be staged?

18 And how would the murder of Vincent be staged?

Act Three

1 What would the audience see at the beginning of Act Three?

2 What sort of character is Maurice?

3 What game do Loll and Jo play during the first flashback in the picnic?

4 What is Mother's reaction to Maurice and Phyllis?

5 What is the plan Walt, Spade and Loll have for Lizzie Berkley?

6 How would the encounter with Lizzie be staged?

7 How would the actress playing Rosie show the character to an audience?

8 What effect does the cider have upon Loll?

9 How would the encounter between Rosie and Loll be staged?

10 How does the tone of the play change after the picnic?

11 How does Mother react to Phyllis wanting to leave home?

12 What is the effect of the fight upon the family?

13 How would the audience react and feel for Mother as she is progressively left alone?

14 Why is it Laurie, not Loll, who has the final scene with Mother?

15 How would the laying out of Mother be staged?

16 How is Loll changed at the end of the play?

17 How is the audience left feeling?

2 Explorations

The questions in this section are more detailed and rely on your having read the whole play. Some of the questions develop ideas from the *Keeping Track* section. Because they tend to be more detailed, they offer the opportunity to develop the ideas into written, oral or practical coursework assignments. Some will require a close knowledge of the play; others will require a more imaginative response.

A Characters

Laurie

1 What is the function of Laurie in the play?

2 How could the character of Laurie show his feelings about the events described in the play?

3 Suggest a costume design for Laurie, paying attention to period and style. Explain your choices and decisions.

4 As an actress or actor, what aspects of the character of Laurie would you wish to highlight for the benefit of an audience? Refer to voice, gesture and movements as appropriate.

Loll

5 How does the character of Loll develop during the course of the play?

6 How would you, as an actress or actor, convey Loll's growth and maturation to an audience? Refer to voice, gesture and movement as appropriate.

7 Suggest a costume design for Loll for each of the three acts. Pay attention both to Loll's age and to the period of the play. Explain your choices and decisions.

8 As an actress or actor, what aspects of the character of Loll would you wish to highlight for the benefit of an audience? Refer to voice, gesture and movement as appropriate.

Mother

9 How does the character of Mother develop during the course of the play?

10 What are her priorities in looking after her family? How does she cope with her situation?

11 Suggest a costume design for Mother. Pay attention to period and style. Explain your choices and decisions.

12 As an actress or actor, what aspects of the character of Mother would you wish to highlight for the benefit of an audience? Refer to voice, movement and gesture as appropriate. If necessary, focus on Act Three in particular.

The family

These questions may be undertaken for any selected member of the family.

13 How does your selected character develop during the course of the play?

14 Suggest a costume design for your chosen character. As before, pay attention to period and style and explain your choices and decisions.

15 As an actress or actor, what aspects of your selected character would you wish to highlight for the benefit of an audience? Refer to voice, gesture and movement as appropriate?

The villagers

Select one of the following characters: Granny Trill, Granny Wallon, Crabby, Spadge Hopkins, Vincent.

16 As an actress or actor, what aspects of your selected character would you wish to highlight for the benefit of an audience? Refer to voice, gesture and movement as appropriate.

17 Suggest an appropriate costume design for your character paying attention to period and style and explaining your choices and decisions.

General

18 Select a character of your choice. Create a monologue for that character in which s/he reflects upon their life and time in the village. Pay attention to how your character reveals his/her thoughts and feelings through your choice of content, manner or expression and choice of vocabulary. (This could then be presented to an audience, who would then ask your character questions, to be answered in role.)

19 Select a character of your choice and write a study of him/her. Refer to speech, actions and interactions as appropriate. How might an audience react to that character?

20 Select a section of the play. Find the relevant section in Lee's original book. Compare the two to discover how Nick Darke has made the adaptation. What changes or developments have been made? Why? How successfully are the characters presented?

B In Performance

1 Select a performance space, such as a drama studio or hall, with which you are familiar. Suggest a setting for the act or scene of your choice from the play.

    Show how you would create appropriate atmosphere in the space available.

2 Suggest a setting which could form the basis of the play as a whole. Pay attention to the requirements of the various scenes and consider how particular items of furniture and props could be used for more than one scene. Consider also how you could convey the period and social setting of the play to the audience.

3 Draw up a list of sound effects needed during the course of the play. Suggest how these might be created for performance.

4 What part would stage lighting play in a successful presentation of *Cider with Rosie*? How in Act Three, for example, could the picnic sequence and its flashbacks be lit and presented to an audience?

5 Select an extract from the play of one scene or more. Rehearse either:

    a   a reading of that extract, ensuring that character and interaction are successfully conveyed to the audience, adding sound effects as necessary.

Or **b**   a presentation of that extract, ensuring that
character and interaction are successfully conveyed
to the audience through your interaction and
pacing of the scene.

6   Select an episode from Laurie Lee's *Cider with Rosie*
and dramatise it, either in your own style or following
the manner of the play. Pay attention to character,
interaction, dialogue and the effect you intend your
piece to have upon your audience. How will you
communicate the nature and tone of the original to
your audience?

C Extended Writing

1   What are the strengths and weaknesses of the
dramatisation of *Cider with Rosie*? Give reasons for your
answers.

2   What picture is presented of village life in this part of
England between the wars? How far, do you think, it is
true to real life?

3   Analyse and evaluate the role and function of Laurie
within the play.

4   In your opinion, how would the play work best: as a
radio play or on the stage? Give reasons for your
answers.

5   Select one character from the play. Write a study of that
character, paying attention to speech and interaction,
suggesting how s/he would be realised in performance.

Further Reading

The three volumes of Laurie Lee's autobiography, of which
Cider with Rosie is the first, are:

Cider with Rosie	Penguin	1959
As I Walked Out One Midsummer Morning	Penguin	1969
A Moment of War	Penguin/Viking	1991

In addition, a volume of his essays and articles entitled
I Can't Stay Long is also published by Penguin and contains
the essay *Writing Autobiography*.

HEINEMANN PLAYS

Joyriders and Did You Hear The One About The Irishman?

Age 14+

Christina Reid

'Mighty Belfast' is the setting for these two plays by Belfast-born playwright, Christina Reid. *Joyriders* is a hard-hitting play about four teenagers from the Divis flats in West Belfast, working on a youth scheme. Through jaunty, tense and often very funny dialogue the teenagers reveal their aspirations and dreams. In *Did You Hear the One About the Irishman?* Alison and Brian's families are linked by marriage but deeply divided by religion. Alison and Brian are warned that their relationship is dangerous but choose to ignore the threat to their lives …

This edition has notes and assignments to help in meeting the requirements of Key Stage 4.

ISBN: 435 23292 4

Journey's End

Age 14+

R C Sherriff

Stanhope is hailed by his men as one of the best Captains in the army. But as he and his officers sit in their dugout awaiting attack, the full horror and futility of trench warfare unfolds. This new edition provides notes and assignments for Key Stage 4.

ISBN: 435 23290 8

The Play of Kes

Age 14+

Barry Hines and Allan Stronach

A straightforward and moving dramatisation of Barry
Hines' novel **Kes** in which fifteen year-old Billy trains a
kestrel. The training of the young hawk inspires feelings
of admiration and affection, emotions which neither his
family nor school offer. This edition comes with new
notes and assignments for Key Stage 4.

ISBN: 435 23288 6

The Play of Flowers for Algernon

Age 14+

Bert Coules

A powerful dramatisation of Daniel Keyes' story. Charlie is a retarded adult who desperately wants to be able to read and write. He undergoes a brain operation which increases his intelligence. But at what cost?

The original short story is included in this edition for comparison work. The play comes complete with notes and assignments to help in meeting the requirements of Key Stage 4.

ISBN: 435 23293 2

The Play of Animal Farm   Age 14+

Peter Hall

This dramatisation of George Orwell's **Animal Farm** is fresh, funny and immensely enjoyable while retaining all the savagery of the original novel. Notes and assignments help in meeting the requirements of Key Stage 4. This edition also comes with lyrics by Adrian Mitchell and music by Richard Peaslee.

ISBN: 435 23291 6

The Best Years Of Your Life & Lives Worth Living

Age 14+

Clive Jermain
Lawrence Evans
Jane Nash

Each of these plays offers frank, perceptive and sometimes humorous insights into the life of a disabled person.

In *The Best Years of Your Life* Robert has cancer of the spine. As a former star of the local football team he finds it difficult to meet his friends while sitting in a wheelchair. Throughout the play, Robert, his father and his brother, work out how to come to terms with his condition.

In *Lives Worth Living* Julie and her mentally-handicapped brother, Mark, are visiting the beach. During one short afternoon we see the whole range of joys and problems being with Mark involves. Through the lively, amusing dialogue between Julie and Mark we see the strong, mutual affection between them.

ISBN: 0435 23294 0

A Taste of Honey

Age 14+

Shelagh Delaney

A new edition of this popular classic play about the complex, conflict ridden relationship between a teenage girl and her mother, and the fleeting moments of affection and escape she finds.

This edition provides notes and assignment suggestions for GCSE.

ISBN: 0435 23299 1

Whose Life is it Anyway?

Brian Clark

Whose Life is it Anyway? is both a powerful stage-play and major feature film about the struggle of the central character for the right to die.

Completely and permanently paralysed by an accident and dependent on a life-support machine, Ken Harrison challenges the traditional duty of the medical profession to keep him alive at all costs.

ISBN: 435 23287 8